GW00865857

Published by:
WRITE THE VISION PUBLISHING LLC
Maumee, Ohio
www.writethevisionpub@gmail.com
writethevisionpub.com

ISBN: 978-1-7344589-7-8 (Hardcover)
ISBN: 978-1-7361006-0-8 (Paperback)
ISBN: 978-1-7344589-8-5 (eBook)

Title: **ARIA'S & GRANDMOMMY'S ADVENTURES – Solving the Mystery of Fire: The Good & The Bad/**
Bonita M. Sparks Adams

Edited by So It Is Written LLC

Illustrations & Cover by Waleed Ahmad

Contributions by Aria Harman

Printed in the United States of America

ARIA'S & GRANDMOMMY'S ADVENTURES

Solving the Mystery of Fire: The Good & The Bad

Written By:

Bonita M. Sparks Adams

Illustrated By:

Waleed Ahmad

Published By:

Write The Vision Publishing LLC

Maumee, OH

DEDICATION

This book is dedicated to my granddaughter, Aria, who has brought such joy to her G-Dad and me. Spending time with you has truly been an adventure.

Words From Aria:

"I hope my family, friends and many others will read this book and be inspired to write their own books."

This book is also dedicated to grandchildren and grandparents everywhere! May you be encouraged to continue to have fun spending quality time together. May you teach valuable lessons, and may you be inspired to create more precious memories with one another.

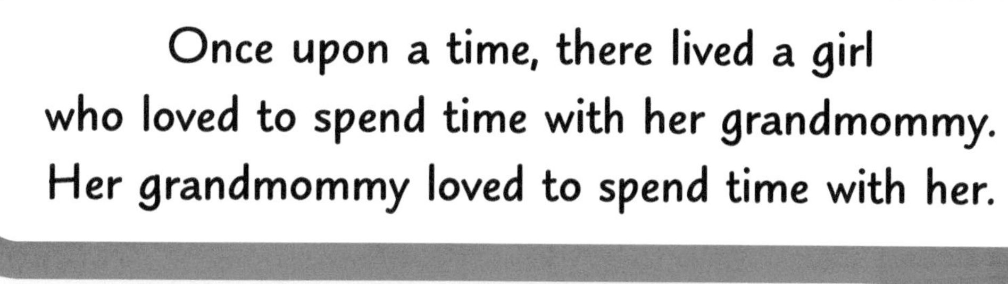
Once upon a time, there lived a girl
who loved to spend time with her grandmommy.
Her grandmommy loved to spend time with her.

Her grandmommy
liked to teach her
new things,
and the girl liked
sharing what
she'd learned.
Let's meet this girl.

Hi!
My name is Aria.
I am a superhero!

When I am with Grandmommy,
I can use my imagination to be
whatever I want to be!

Don't let
my age fool you.
I have many
superpowers.
Did you know that
I can melt hearts?

At least that's what Grandmommy and G-Dad believe when I give them a hug.
GM

Today's adventure will be to find out good things and bad things about fire.

Grandmommy showed me
that fire is good because
it helps us cook our food.
We made cookies together!
Yummy!
GM

Grandmommy showed me that fire is good because it provides us with heat and light. We went over Nana & Granddaddy's house. Their fireplace kept the house warm and lit up the entire room.

GM
Grandmommy showed me that fire can melt things or keep things hot. We made hot chocolate. It was so hot that all the marshmallows melted!

Did you know love is a superpower like fire, too? It can melt away bad things.

Showing love for
my parents by
helping around
the house...

is like a
SUPERPOWER
that makes them
feel better.
It "melts" away
bad feelings
about having
a dirty house.
BAD
FEELINGS

Showing love
for my family by
making cards for
them or calling
them on the
phone...

is like a SUPERPOWER that makes them happy. It "melts" away feelings of sadness because we live so far away from each other.
SAD FEELINGS

Showing love
to my cousins and
friends by playing
nice and not
being mean...

is like a
SUPERPOWER
that "melts" away
bad feelings.
It helps us to
get along.
BAD
FEELINGS

It is not good
to be mean or to
do bad things to people
who do bad things to us.

It just makes
bad feelings grow
EVEN BIGGER.

To help us solve
THE MYSTERY OF FIRE:
The Good & The Bad,
we went to visit our cousin,
Fire Chief Brian!
GM

Since I AM
A SUPERHERO,
and superheroes
help people,
I want to help
you by sharing
some other things
I learned from
Fire Chief Brian.

Fire is hot.
You should
not try to pick up
hot things.

Never pick up or play with
matches or lighters.
If you see them, tell an adult.
Point to it or show them where it is.

A fire can grow
fast and spread
quickly.
Stay back, and
don't get close
to the fire.

If there is a fire
where you are,
you should get
out and stay out!

If you catch on fire...

Stop, Drop & Roll!

Ask your parents to show you a smoke detector in your house, and to let you hear how it sounds.

Ask your parents to
practice your plan of escape
in case you ever have
a fire in your house.

The MYSTERY
has been solved!

I learned that fire has some good benefits. But, it also can be bad and dangerous, too! I must follow the rules to stay safe!

Firemen, like my cousin
Fire Chief Brian, are also superheroes.
They are your friends and they protect
you from the dangers of fire.

If you want to be
A SUPERHERO,
help others. Show love.
Follow rules and avoid
the bad things
I talked about today.

You can go on adventures with your grandmommy or G-Dad, too! What fun things will you learn about or do with each other?

I hope you will join Grandmommy and me on our next adventure! Bye, bye for now!
GM

Picture by Aria Harman

"Dear Reader,

I hope after you read this book,

you want to make your own book too."

— Aria Harman, Age 5